Photographs by Howard Allman

Contents

Bright bugs

Print a bee's body, then paint the wings and stripes.

Spread the paint into a long thin shape.

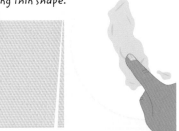

1. Cut a long triangle from the edge of a kitchen sponge cloth. Using your finger, spread some thick green paint on an old plate. Then, wash your hands.

To print a butterfly, cut an egg shape for the wings and a long pointed shape for the body.

Print an oval for a spider's body and a circle for its head.

For slightly opened wings, like those on the bug below, print two half circles overlapping.

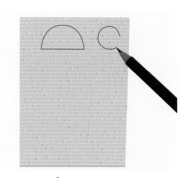

Leave room for a beetle between the blades of grass.

2. To print blades of grass, lay the triangle in the paint. Press all over it, then lift it out and lay it on a piece of paper. Press it again, then lift it off and print a second one.

3. For a beetle's body, draw half a circle on the sponge cloth with a thin felt-tip pen. Draw a small circle for the head, then cut out both shapes.

Leave a gap for the legs between the body and the grass.

4. Using thick pink paint, print the body a little way away from the grass. Then, print a purple head, overlapping the body. Leave the paint to dry.

Use bright paints for the legs, feelers and stripes.

5. Using a thin paintbrush, add white circles for eyes. Rinse your brush, then add legs and feelers. Rinse your brush again, then add stripes on the body.

6. Leave the paint to dry completely. Then, use a black pen to draw dots on the eyes for pupils. Add a little curve for a smiling mouth, too.

For a caterpillar, cut out a circle, then print it again and again to make a long body.

Tall giraffe picture

Draw the head near the top of the paper.

Fingerprint over the pencil lines, like this.

1. Draw a shape for a giraffe's head on a piece of thick paper. Add stubby horns, an ear and a long neck. Then, erase the lines shown here in red.

2. Pour orange and white paints onto an old plate. Fingerprint markings down the giraffe's neck. Print a white eye using the eraser on the end of a pencil.

Print markings like these with an eraser.

3. When the paint is dry, cut out the giraffe and glue it onto a piece of paper. Use pens to add a mouth, eyelashes and a dot in the eye for a pupil.

This giraffe was drawn on white paper and markings were added with a white wax crayon. Watery yellow paint was brushed on top.

There are lots of different ways to make markings on a giraffe – look at this picture for ideas.

Fingerprinted markings

This giraffe was filled in with yellow paint. The brown markings were dabbed on while the paint was wet.

You could just paint the markings.

You can print markings with bubble wrap — see steps 2-5 on page 10.

These markings were printed using a square of sponge cloth dipped into thick orange paint.

These spots were printed with an eraser on the end of a pencil.

Fingerprinted animals

1. Cut a small rectangle from a kitchen sponge cloth and lay it on an old newspaper. Brush thick paint onto part of the sponge, so that it soaks in a little.

2. To make a fingerprint, press the end of one of your fingers into the paint. Press it down a few times until your finger is covered with a layer of paint.

3. Press your finger onto a piece of paper to make fingerprints. When the paint is dry, use the ideas on these pages to draw different animals with a thin black pen.

Press your finger into the paint again if the prints become too pale.

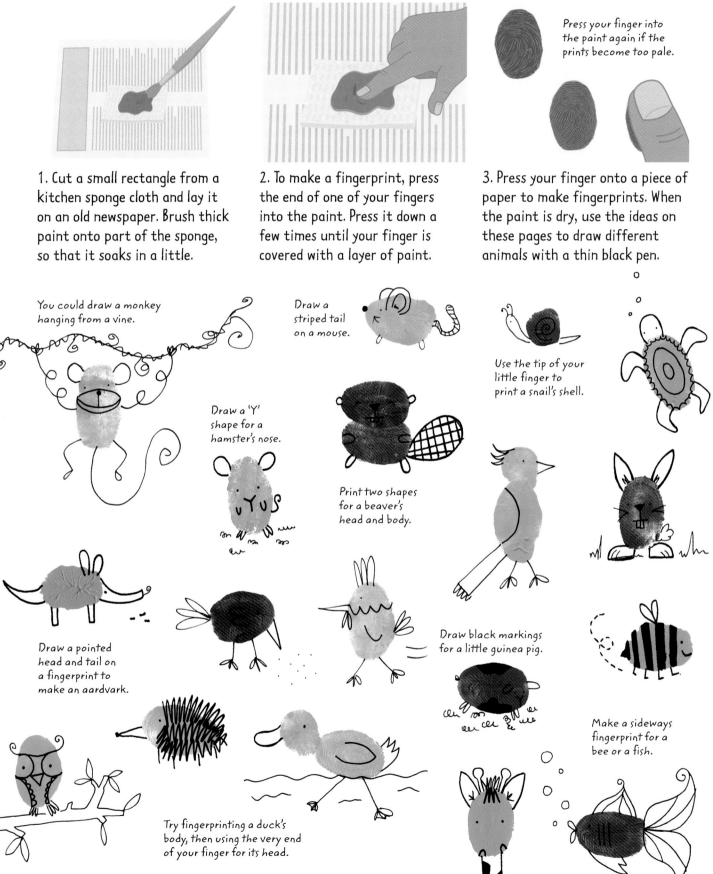

You could draw a monkey hanging from a vine.

Draw a striped tail on a mouse.

Use the tip of your little finger to print a snail's shell.

Draw a 'Y' shape for a hamster's nose.

Print two shapes for a beaver's head and body.

Draw a pointed head and tail on a fingerprint to make an aardvark.

Draw black markings for a little guinea pig.

Make a sideways fingerprint for a bee or a fish.

Try fingerprinting a duck's body, then using the very end of your finger for its head.

6

Make two prints with the tip of your finger for a horse's neck.

Draw lots of looping lines around a lion's head for its mane.

The head and body of this walrus are thumbprints.

Draw curly antlers on a reindeer.

This crocodile is a mixture of thumb, finger and fingertip prints, pressed more and more lightly along its tail.

You could draw a raccoon with a mask and a pointed tail.

Make two lines of prints for a hippo's body.

Draw spots and a mane on a giraffe.

7

Stand-up animals

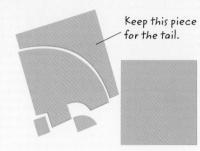

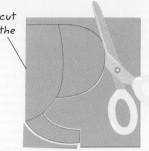

Fold ——

Draw these shapes for the body and legs.

Keep this piece for the tail.

Don't cut along the fold.

1. To make an elephant's body, fold a rectangle of thick paper in half. Cut a narrow triangle off the bottom. Then, draw a body and legs against the fold.

2. Holding the layers together, cut out the body and legs, but don't cut along the fold. Then, fold a second paper rectangle in half for the head.

3. Draw a shape for the head against the fold. Then, add an ear and a curving trunk. Cut out the whole shape, through both layers. Then, unfold the head and body.

You can make a polar bear by cutting these shapes from white paper.

You could make one of these animals and send it as a birthday card. Write your message on the back.

4. Cut off one of the trunks. Then, draw outlines around the head and body, like this. Draw dots for eyes, a squiggle on the trunk, and toenails on the feet.

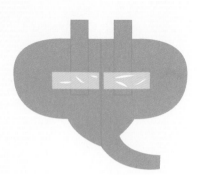

5. To make the head stand out from the body, cut two short strips of paper. Tape one end of each strip onto the back of the head, like this.

6. Lay the body on the head, like this. Then, curl the end of one of the paper strips over onto the body and tape it on. Do the same with the other strip.

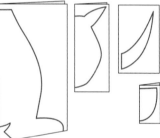

To make a kangaroo, cut out the shapes above for its body, head and tail, and a little folded shape for its pouch.

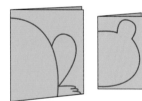

These two shapes will make a stand-up frog.

Glue around the edge of the kangaroo's pouch, to make it stick out a little.

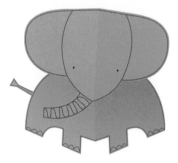

7. Draw a tail on a scrap of the paper and cut it out. Tape it onto the back of the body. Then, turn the elephant over and fold it so that it stands up.

Printed crocodile

Don't cover the crocodile's head.

Make sure you brush paint on all the bumps.

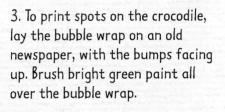

1. Draw a rectangle on green paper for a crocodile's body. Add two legs and a long tail. Draw the head with bumps for the eye and nostril. Add more little bumps along its back.

2. Cut out the crocodile and turn it over. Cut a rectangle of bubble wrap that is big enough to cover the crocodile's body, tail and legs, like this.

3. To print spots on the crocodile, lay the bubble wrap on an old newspaper, with the bumps facing up. Brush bright green paint all over the bubble wrap.

Rubbing the bubble wrap helps to print the paint onto the crocodile.

Hold the crocodile with one hand as you peel off the bubble wrap.

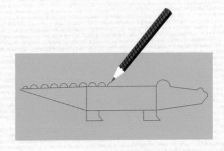

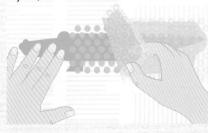

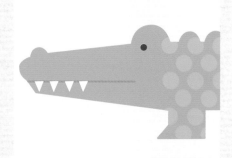

4. Lay the crocodile on some newspaper. Then, lay the bubble wrap, with the bumps facing down, over the crocodile again. Press it down, then rub it gently.

5. Starting at one end, carefully peel the bubble wrap off the crocodile without smudging the spots. Then, leave the paint to dry completely.

6. Draw an eye and a line for a mouth with felt-tip pens. Cut small triangles from white paper for the teeth, then glue them along the mouth.

Ant-eating aardvark

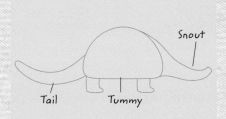

1. For the aardvark's body, use a pencil to draw a rounded shape with a flat tummy, in the middle of a piece of paper. Press lightly as you draw.

2. Draw a long snout at one end of the body shape, and add a curving tail at the other end. Then, draw a short leg at each end of the aardvark's tummy.

3. Draw two ears sticking up. Then, carefully erase all the lines inside the outline. Draw a round eye with a black felt-tip pen. Then, cut out the aardvark.

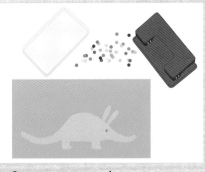

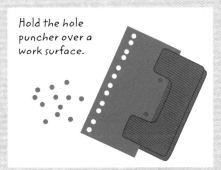

Hold the hole puncher over a work surface.

4. Glue the aardvark near the bottom of a large piece of paper. Then, take the bottom off a hole puncher and throw away any paper circles inside.

5. Leave the bottom off the hole puncher, then use it to punch lots of holes along the edges of a piece of dark brown paper. The circles will make the ants' bodies.

6. Glue three of the paper circles in a line for an ant's body. Then, use a black pencil to draw legs and feelers. Add more ants running around the aardvark.

You could add an ant running along the aardvark's back.

An aardvark uses its snout to sniff out ants living in the ground. It digs them out, then licks them up with its long sticky tongue.

Friendly lion collage

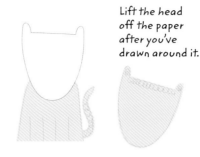

1. Using an orange pencil, draw a lion's head and ears on thick paper. Draw the body, legs and tail. Then, add curls for fur on the tail, head and inside the ears.

Lift the head off the paper after you've drawn around it.

2. Cut out the body and tail, leaving a thin border around the edge. Glue the shape onto a piece of paper. Cut out the head, then lay it on the paper and draw around it.

Paint over the outline a little.

3. Draw wavy shapes for a mane around the head outline. Draw fur on the end of the tail, too. Fill the mane and fur with thick brown paint. Leave the paint to dry.

Overlap the pieces a little.

Glue part of each circle over the muzzle.

4. For the lion's muzzle, cut out a rectangle and an oval from a picture of hair or fur from an old magazine. Glue on the rectangle, then glue the oval on top.

5. Cut two circles for the cheeks from pink paper. Then, use a pink pencil to scribble around and around on the circles. Glue them on either side of the muzzle.

6. For eyes, glue on little black beads or draw dots. Draw a line and a curve for the mouth with a black pen. Cut two teeth from white paper, then glue them on.

7. Cut lots of pieces of thread or yarn for the mane. For each curl, spread thick white glue on part of the mane. Coil a piece of thread into a spiral and press it on.

8. When the glue is dry, turn the face over and carefully spread glue all over it. Lay the face onto your picture, so that it fits inside the mane, and press it all over.

Press the nose until it sticks.

9. For the nose, cut a long piece of thread or yarn. Spread a big oval of thick white glue on the muzzle. Twist the thread into a ball and press it onto the glue.

Wobbling penguins

You don't need the egg white or yolk, but you could use them for cooking.

1. Tap the middle of an egg sharply on the rim of a mug to crack it. Then, use your fingers to break the egg carefully in half over the mug.

The weight of the poster tack makes the penguin wobble.

2. Wash the eggshell, then let it dry completely. Using white glue, glue a ball of poster tack into the middle of the bottom half of the shell, like this.

3. Leave the glue to dry. Then, cut several short thin strips of any shade of tissue paper. Lay them on an old newspaper and brush glue all over one side of them.

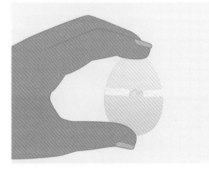

4. Hold the bottom of the eggshell and gently fit the other half on top, matching the edges as well as you can. Then, press the strips of tissue paper along the join.

5. Rip more tissue paper into lots of little pieces. Brush part of the egg with thick white glue. Then, press pieces of tissue paper onto the wet glue.

6. Glue on more tissue paper until the egg is covered and leave it to dry on a piece of plastic foodwrap. Then, paint the egg with thick black paint and let it dry.

If you push your penguin gently it will wobble from side to side.

Don't cut along the fold.

Cutting out
the shape
makes two
wings.

7. Paint a shape for the penguin's face and tummy with thick white paint. Then, when the paint is dry, add two black spots for eyes with the tip of a brush.

8. To make a beak, fold a scrap of orange paper in half. Draw a 'V' coming down from the fold, then cut it out. Spread glue on the fold and press the beak onto the egg.

9. Fold a piece of black paper in half, and draw a wing. Holding the layers together, cut out the shape. Then, glue the flat end of each wing onto the sides of the penguin.

The baby penguins in this photo were made using quails' eggs instead of hens' eggs.

15

Fieldmice collage

Overlap the
shapes for
the grain.

1. Cut a stalk and leaf shapes
for grain from yellow and brown
paper. Glue the stalk onto a piece
of paper. Then, glue on the grain,
starting at the top of the stalk.

Glue on the
ears so that
they overlap,
like this.

2. Cut a mouse's body and two ears
from paper. Glue one ear onto the
back of the body and the other one
on top. Then, draw a dot for an eye
with a black felt-tip pen.

You could make
a picture like
this, with mice
on several stalks.

Add some
pink lines
inside the
ear, too.

3. Spread some glue onto the back
of the mouse's body, then press it
onto the stalk. Cut a circle for a
nose and glue it on. Then, draw a
curling tail with a pink pencil.

16

Bird doodles

Most of the birds around the edges of this page were made by mixing shapes from the steps.

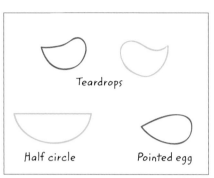

Teardrops

Half circle   Pointed egg

1. Using bright pencils, draw lots of shapes for birds' bodies on white paper. Draw teardrops, half circles and pointed eggs. Leave spaces in between the shapes.

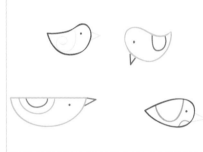

2. Use different pencils to draw dots for eyes and triangles for beaks. Then, add curves and spirals for wings. You could add a curve for a tummy, too.

3. Draw little loops and curly lines for the birds' tails. Add wiggly feathers on the heads of some of the birds, too. Then, draw their legs and feet.

You could draw long curly tail feathers.

You could draw birds singing or eating grain.

17

3-D turtles

You could decorate a turtle's shell with two shades of green paint, or even shiny gold paint.

Use a pencil.

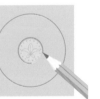

1. For the turtle's shell, draw around a mug on a piece of paper. Lift off the mug, then lay a large coin in the middle of the circle and draw around it.

Don't draw inside the small circle.

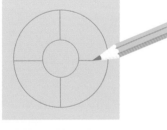

2. Draw a line going from the edge of the small circle to the edge of the big circle. Then, draw three more lines, spacing them evenly so that it looks like this.

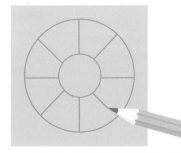

3. Draw lines in the spaces in between the lines you drew in step 2. Space them out as evenly as you can. You should end up with eight lines altogether.

Lay the circle on an old newspaper.

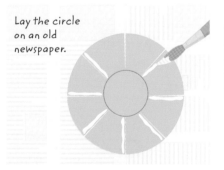

4. Cut around the big circle. Then, cut along the straight lines, but don't cut around the small circle. Brush a line of thick white glue along one edge of each section.

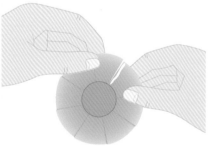

5. To make the shell 3-D, slide the edge of one section over the glue on the one next to it. Hold it until it sticks, then overlap all the other sections in the same way.

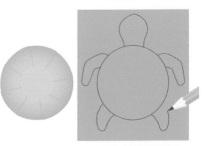

6. To make the body, turn the shell over. Lay it on a piece of thick paper. Draw around it, then lift off the shell. Draw a turtle's head and four flippers around the circle.

18

To make a baby turtle, draw around a small glass instead of a mug.

7. Cut out the turtle and turn it over. Brush a circle of thick white glue around the body, like this. Then, press the edges of the shell onto the circle of wet glue.

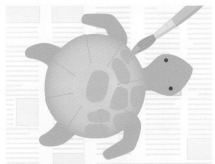

8. Leave the glue to dry. Then, draw two black dots for eyes. Using a thin paintbrush, paint patterns on the turtle's shell. Then, leave the paint to dry.

19

Hungry shark picture

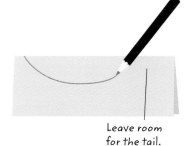

Leave room for the tail.

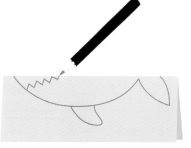

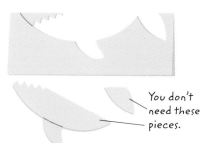

This piece is the stencil.

You don't need these pieces.

1. To make a shark stencil, fold a rectangle of thick paper in half along its length. With the fold at the top, draw a curved shape for a shark's body.

2. Draw a shape for a shark's tail at the end of the body and add a curved fin underneath the body. Then, draw a zigzag line for teeth, like this.

3. Cut along the zigzag line. Then, cut around the body, fin and tail. Open out the stencil, run your finger along the fold to flatten it, then put the stencil aside.

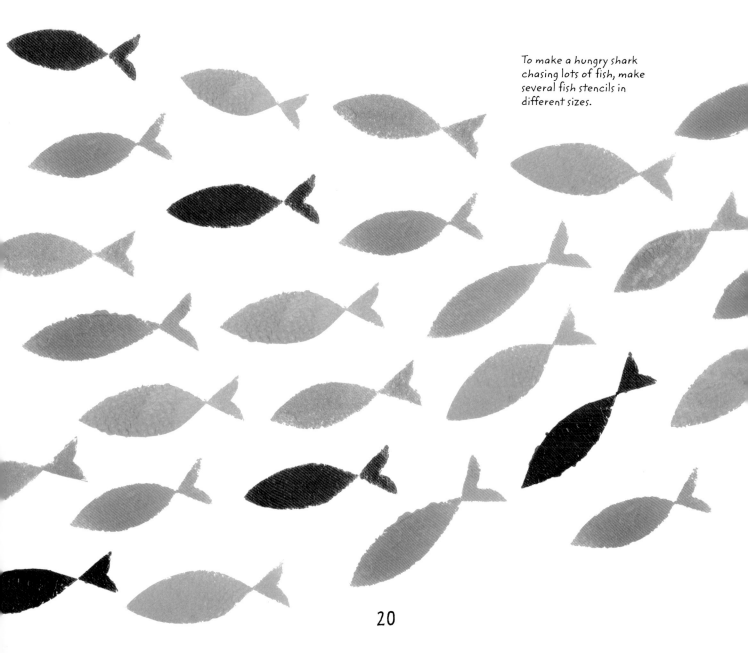

To make a hungry shark chasing lots of fish, make several fish stencils in different sizes.

20

If you're using several shades of paint, make a different stencil for each one.

Leave room for a fish here.

Use a thin paintbrush.

4. To make a fish stencil, fold a smaller piece of thick paper in half. Draw a curved body and a tail, like this. Then, cut out the shapes and unfold the stencil.

5. Lay the shark stencil on a piece of paper. Spread thick paint on an old plate. Then, dip a sponge into the paint and dab it again and again over the hole in the stencil.

6. Continue dabbing on the paint until the shark is filled in. Lift off the stencil. Then, add a fish in front of the shark. When the paint is dry, paint an eye on the shark.

21

Animals at a waterhole

1. To make a zebra, fold a rectangle of thick white paper in half. Fold up the bottom of the paper to make flaps for the base. Then, fold the flaps down again.

2. Use a pencil to draw the zebra's body, legs and tail above the flaps. Then, draw two tabs on the flaps, below the legs. They will become a base for the zebra to stand on.

3. Draw a head on another piece of paper. Then, go over all of the lines with a black felt-tip pen. Add stripes on the zebra's head, body, legs and tail.

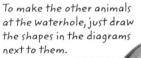
Keep the paper folded.

Glue the square near the front of the body.

4. Cut out the head. Then, cut around the tail and back leg. Cut around the rest of the body, including the pencil lines for the tabs. Don't cut along the fold.

5. Fold the tabs under the body. Then, spread glue on one of the tabs on the back leg and press it onto the other tab. Do the same with the front leg tabs.

6. To attach the zebra's head, cut a small square from thick cardboard. Glue it onto the body, like this. Then, glue the head onto the square.

To make the other animals at the waterhole, just draw the shapes in the diagrams next to them.

Hippo

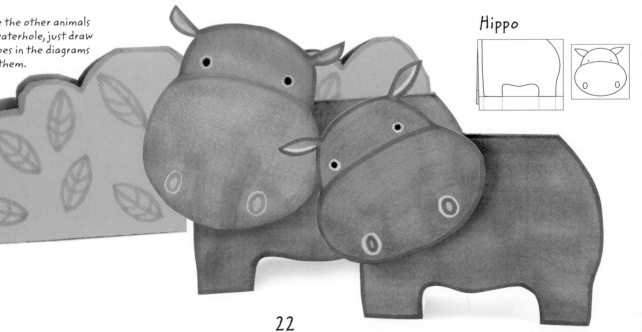

Giraffe

Tree

Elephant

Lion

Bush

Cut and stick owls

Leave room on the paper for an owl to sit on the branch.

1. Draw a branch on a piece of purple paper. Cut it out and glue it onto a large piece of paper. Cut leaves from green paper and glue them on, too.

You could make a big picture, with lots of owls sitting on long branches.

2. To make a template so that you can draw shapes for the pieces of the owl, draw an oval on a piece of thin cardboard. Add pointed ears, then cut around the shape.

3. Lay the template on a piece of patterned paper and draw around it with a pencil. Then, lift off the template. Cut out the owl and glue it onto the branch.

You could use wrapping paper or paper from an old magazine.

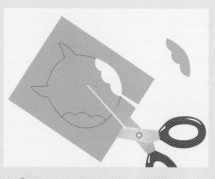

4. For wings, draw around the template on plain paper. Lift it off, then draw wings inside the outline. Cut out the wings, then glue them onto the owl.

You could use plain and patterned papers for the leaves.

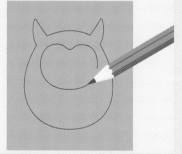

5. Draw around the template again on another piece of plain paper, then lift it off. Draw a shape for the owl's face inside the outline, then cut it out.

6. Glue the face onto the owl. Then, cut two white circles and two smaller blue circles for eyes. Glue the blue circles in the middle of the white circles, like this.

7. Using a black felt-tip pen, draw a dot in the middle of each eye for a pupil. Glue the eyes onto the face. Then, cut out a yellow beak and glue it on, too.

25

Clinging koala

These branches were cut from cardboard and then painted. Paper leaves were glued on top.

Draw the head and ears near the top of the paper.

1. To make the koala's body sturdy, fold a rectangle of paper in half. Unfold it and spread glue on one side, then press the layers together. Then, draw a koala's head and ears.

2. Draw a rounded body and two legs. Cut a paper strip for the arms, making it as tall as the koala. Then, cut around the koala and turn it over.

3. Draw a face with a black felt-tip pen. Using pencils, scribble lots of zigzag lines on the koala for its fur. Scribble all over one side of the paper strip, too.

4. For the arms, cut a piece of pipe cleaner the same length as the paper strip. Fold the strip in half along its length, then unfold it and spread glue on it.

Draw curves for a sleeping koala's eyes.

Lay the pipe cleaner on the fold, like this...

...then fold the strip back over it, like this.

5. Lay the pipe cleaner along the fold. Then, fold the strip over and line up the edges. Press down the top layer and rub it gently until the glue sticks.

6. To make a slot for the arms to go through, gently pinch the koala's body with your fingers, like this. Use scissors to snip a short cut into the body.

Push the arms halfway through the cut, like this.

7. Using your scissors, make the cut a little longer, so that the arms will fit through it. Push the arms through the cut, then tape them onto the back of the body.

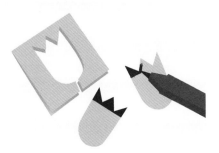

8. Fold a piece of paper in half and draw a paw on it. Cut out the shape, through both layers. Then, draw claws on both paws with a black felt-tip pen.

9. Bend the arms around to the front of the koala and glue on the paws. Then, bend the arms around more tightly, so that the koala can cling to things.

27

Cat and dog drawings
Fluffy cat

Fill in the stripe.

Draw a little pink tongue, too.

1. Use an orange pencil to draw a cat's head and ears. Draw a triangular body below the head. Add two legs and a long tail. Then, draw a stripe down the face.

2. Draw around the face with zigzag lines. Fill in the ears, too. Then, draw zigzags on the body and tail. Fill in the legs, too. Add a nose, mouth, eyes and whiskers.

You could fill all of a cat's face.

Use the ideas on these pages to draw lots of different cats and dogs.

For a running cat, draw a triangle on its side, then add the head, legs and tail.

Draw a little triangle for a mouse, then add ears, paws, a face and a tail.

This yellow cat is licking its fur.

You could draw a sleeping cat with a rectangle instead of a triangle for a body.

Draw curved lines for the eyes of a sleeping dog.

You could draw a tall dog with really long legs.

This dog has such long fur that you can't see its legs.

You could draw a collar on your dog.

Scribble around and around for a poodle's curly fur.

For a dog sitting down, draw short back legs on either side of its body.

You can make dogs look very different by drawing different shapes for their heads.

Friendly dog

1. Using a pale pencil, draw a curved shape for a dog's head. Draw a large rectangle for the body and add a curved tail. Then, draw four legs and fill them in.

2. Draw markings on the head and body with a brown pencil. Fill in the dog's head, body and tail. Then, use a black pencil to draw two dots for eyes, a nose, and two ears.

29

Monkey chain

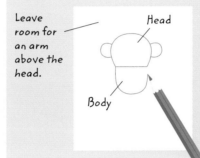

1. To make a template so that you can make several monkeys, draw a curve and a line for the head on a piece of thin cardboard. Add ears, then draw a body below the head.

Leave room for an arm above the head.

Head

Body

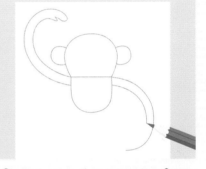

2. Draw a curved arm coming from each side of the monkey's body. Make the arm on the left curve up, and the arm on the right curve down, like this.

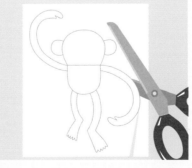

3. Draw one leg at the bottom of the body. Then, add the other leg, making it a little longer than the first one. Carefully cut around the template.

4. Cut three squares from thick brown paper. Lay the template on each square and carefully draw around it. Then, lift it off and cut out the monkeys.

Hold down the arms and legs as you draw.

To make a picture like this, glue the ends of pieces of string onto cardboard and add paper leaves. Hang the monkeys over the string.

You could draw a banana and glue it onto a monkey's hand, like this.

You can find banana and leaf stickers on the sticker pages.

Draw this shape for the face.

The bottom monkey had its face glued on the other side of the paper so that it hangs the other way.

5. To make faces for the monkeys, lay the template on a piece of thin cardboard. Draw around the head and ears, then lift it off. Draw a face shape inside the outline.

6. Cut out the face. Then, draw around it on three pieces of paper. Cut out the shapes and glue one onto each monkey. Draw faces on them with a thin brown pen.

7. Pin one of the monkeys onto a pinboard or hang it over a door handle. Hang another monkey from its hand, then add another one at the bottom.

Spotted sea lions

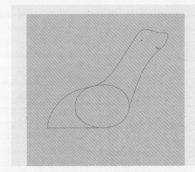

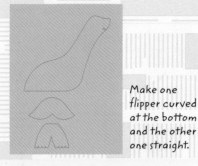

Make one flipper curved at the bottom and the other one straight.

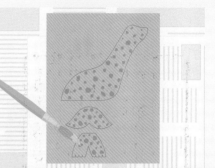

1. For a sea lion, draw an oval for the body on a piece of thick paper. Then, add its bottom, head and neck. Draw a mouth, too. Then, erase the oval.

2. Draw shapes for the flippers. Make one about the width of the sea lion's body, and the other a little narrower. Then, lay the paper on an old newspaper.

3. Mix thick white glue with water to make it runny. Using an old paintbrush, dab lots of glue spots onto the three shapes. Then, leave the glue to dry.

Cut out the mouth, too.

4. Draw an eye and a nose. Then, cut out the body and flippers. To make the sea lion stand up, cut slits in the shapes (shown here in red) and slot the flippers onto the body.

To make a sea lion eating a fish, cut a fish from shiny paper, cut a slit in it and slide it into the sea lion's mouth.

Photographic manipulation by John Russell and Nick Wakeford.
This edition first published in 2013 by Usborne Publishing Ltd.,
Usborne House, 83-85 Saffron Hill, London, England. www.usborne.com